POEMS FOR THE RETIRED

Published in 2005

by Fortune Teller Press

(0-9547737-1-3)

This book Copyright © Fortune Teller Press. 2005

All rights reserved. No part of this publication may be reproduced, transmitted, or stored in a retrieval system etc etc. No poem shall appear on the web, without permission. This book is sold on the condition that you read and appreciate every single poem that has been painstakingly included. No part of this publication must be used for advertising, sales promotion or publicity.

....

Compiled by G. Bendel

Front cover painting by Tina Vaughan.

Other artwork by Tina Vaughan
(pages: 19, 40, 42, 53, 79, 89)

and Robert Johnson
(pages: 11, 14, 38)

and Keith Bendel
(page 52)

Printed by Antony Rowe Limited.

....

www.fortunetellerpress.com

Email: info@fortunetellerpress.com

Paul Birtill's Poem, "God Works in Mysterious Ways", was taken from *Collected Poems 1987-2003* (published by Hearing Eye). Paul was born in Liverpool.

"Blues" By Edward Kamau Braithwaite from BLACK AND BLUES., copyright © 1976, 1994, 1995 by Kamau Braithwaite. Reprinted by permission of New Directions Publishing Corp.

Thanks to Ian McCorquodale and Cartland Promotions for granting permission for Barbara Cartland's poem, To A Pekinese .

Harmony Korine's "Rumors" (abridged) is taken from *A Crack-Up At The Race Riots*, published by Faber & Faber.

Mervyn Peake's poem "The Vastest Things Are Those We May Not Learn" is taken from Selected Poems, published by Faber and Faber Ltd. Mervyn Peake is the writer of *Gormenghast* and *Titus Groan*.

James Lineberger is a professional US playwright.and screenwriter. He wrote the screenplay for *Taps* (1981). A full-time poet now, his output is prolific.

Danny McCosh lives in the UK.

Daniel Joshua Nagelberg is the writer of *The Anger Report*, published by SevenTen Bishop in the US.

Nina Antonia has written books about The New York Dolls and Johnny Thunders. The featured extract is from her latest book, entitled *The Prettiest Star* (SAF Publishing).

Penny Rimbaud was a founder of the infamous UK Anarchist Punk band, CRASS. He is a performance poet.

Nikki Giovanni was born in Knoxville, Tennessee, and is a world-renowned poet, writer, commentator, activist, and educator. Her poem Ego Tripping also appears on a funk compilation, I'm a Good Woman 2 (Harmless).

Owen O'Neill is a comedian, actor and poet. The poem Broken is taken from *Volcano Dancing*, published by Thirsty Books.

Benjamin Zephaniah is one of Britain's best poets. His poem Anti-Slavery Movements is taken from *Too Black, Too Strong* (reproduced by permission of Bloodaxe).

The Pam Ayres Appreciation Society is the brainchild of one very lonely and sick man.

Whitman McGowan is a cult San Francisco performance poet, who has collaborated with Maya Angelou and Coldcut. Two of his poems are featured in this anthology.

"Egocentric"
By Stevie Smith, from COLLECTED POEMS OF STEVIE SMITH, copyright © 1972 by Stevie Smith. Reprinted by permission of New Directions Publishing Corp.

Eric Bogosian is an actor and novelist. He starred in Oliver Stone's *Talk Radio* and was also in Woody Allen's *Deconstructing Harry*. His first novel was *Mall*.

"So You Want to be A Writer" from SIFTING THROUGH THE MADNESS FOR THE WORD, THE LINE, THE WAY: NEW POEMS by CHARLES BUKOWKSI and EDITED BY JOHN MARTIN
Copyright © 2003 by Linda Lee Bukowski. Reprinted by Permission of HarperCollins Publishers Inc.

"Daddy" is taken from *Ariel* by Sylvia Plath and has been licensed from Faber and Faber Ltd.

Late-Flowering Lust by Sir John Betjeman has been taken from *Collected Poems* by John Betjeman. It was reproduced by permission of John Murray Publishers.

Graham Martin comes from Wembley and sometimes hides from people in the big branch of Asda.

Mark Hartenbach tries to maintain his sanity in a small Appalachian town along the ohio river. his latest books are *Book of Resurrection* & *Beyond the Valley of the Blue-Eyed Boys* from pudding house press.

GG Allin recorded 'Layin' Up With Linda' in 1993, with the Carolina Shitkickers.

Marie Kazalia's poem Sixteen was first published in *Slipstream Magazine*. She is from San Francisco and published by The Red Hand Press.

"Winter In The City of Friendship" By Mary Karr, from THE DEVIL'S TOUR, copyright © 1993 by Mary Karr. Reprinted by permission of New Directions Publishing Corp.

Fran Landesman is a songwriter and poet laureate of lovers and losers. Her husband Jay Landesman is often credited with 'starting it all'. He published Kerouac and Ginsberg in his seminal magazine, *Neurotica*.

"Sometime During Eternity (#5)" By Lawrence Ferlinghetti, from A CONEY ISLAND OF THE MIND, copyright © 1958 by Lawrence Ferlinghetti. Ferlinghetti was the founder of City Lights, who published Ginsberg (and his infamous *Howl*), and also many others. He was namechecked in the film *Educating Rita*.

Richard Hell has been in Television, Richard Hell and The Voidoids and Johnny Thunder's Heartbreakers. He is a writer of novels and poetry. The excerpt of 'Autobiography Of A Small, Mean Man (1)' is taken from *Hot and Cold* (published by powerHouse). His latest novel *Godlike* is published by Akashic Books.

Lord Alfred Douglas was commonly known as Bosie, and was a *friend* of Oscar Wilde. His poem The Travelling Companion (1899) is taken from *City of the Soul*. Copyright © : the executors of the Lord Alfred Douglas Literary Estate.

June Hird is the mother of Scottish writer Laura Hird. '*Dear Laura*', a selection of June's letters to her daughter, and a study of the mother/daughter relationship, is currently in progress.

Steven Berkoff is a writer and actor. *'From My Point Of View'* is taken from Gross Intrusion and Other Stories (© 1979, 1993).

'All rights whatsoever in this play is strictly reserved. Applications for performance, including professional, amateur, recitation, lecturing, public reading, broadcasting, television and the rights of translation into foreign languages, should be made before rehearsals begin to Rosica Colin Ltd, 1 Clareville Grove Mews, London SW7 5AH. No performance may be given unless a licence has been obtained'.

CONTENTS

Broken

by Owen O'Neill

'They say a rock can split if it's hot enough.'
The stubbled man talked about this
in the bar.

She was the only woman in there.
She said her mother died of a broken heart
but no one heard her.

'Split right down the middle. So big you could
crawl inside. It's the heat, an aboriginal told me.
Saw it with his own eyes.'

She said her mother never opened the curtains again.
Couldn't bear to see another living thing.
The cat was mad with hunger when they found her.

'Doesn't matter how hard it is!' He was shouting
now, the beer was catching him, it was on his tail.
'In fact the harder the better!'

When they found her she was dressed in his clothes
even had his working boots on. Her tired little
feet, at peace, inside those size tens.

'They say when it cracks!. . .There's a holy terror
of a sound. . .like ripping thunder!
And then. . . and then the rain comes.'

She said it rained that day. . .
it just...rained...and rained...and rained
didn't stop.

So You Want To Be A Writer?

Charles Bukowski

if it doesn't come bursting out of you
in spite of everything,
don't do it.
unless it comes unasked out of your
heart and your mind and your mouth
and your gut,
don't do it.
if you have to sit for hours
staring at your computer screen
or hunched over your
typewriter
searching for words,
don't do it.
if you're doing it for money or
fame,
don't do it.
if you're doing it because you want
women in your bed,
don't do it.
if you have to sit there and
rewrite it again and again,
don't do it.
if it's hard work just thinking about doing it,
don't do it.
if you're trying to write like somebody
else,
forget about it.

if you have to wait for it to roar out of
you, then wait patiently.

if it never does roar out of you,
do something else.
if you first have to read it to your wife
or your girlfriend or your boyfriend
or your parents or to anybody at all,
you're not ready.

don't be like so many writers,
don't be like so many thousands of
people who call themselves writers,
don't be dull and boring and
pretentious, don't be consumed with self-
love.
the libraries of the world have
yawned themselves to
sleep
over your kind.
don't add to that.
don't do it.
unless it comes out of
your soul like a rocket,
unless being still would
drive you to madness or
suicide or murder,
don't do it.
unless the sun inside you is
burning your gut,
don't do it.

when it is truly time,
and if you have been chosen,
it will do it by
itself and it will keep on doing it
until you die or it dies in
you.

there is no other way.

and there never was.

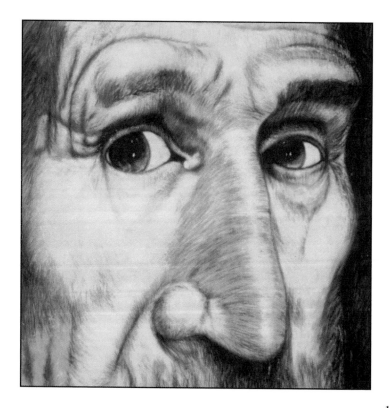

Drunken Coachman

Arthur Rimbaud

Drunk
Skunk
Stars
Sees.

Harsh
Law:
Coach →
Trees.

Girl
Hurled,
Much

Blood.
Boo
Hoo!

TO A PEKINESE

Barbara Cartland

You were so soft, so sweet, so small,
And yet you gave your heart and all
Your love - until you died
Walking along the wrong side
Of the road.

The car didn't stop and I found you there.
Your eyes were closed and your long white fur
Was covered in blood and you didn't stir
When I called.

Such a little life, so little time
To live and yet you were part of mine.
And I never can walk in the mud and rain
Without seeing you lying dead again
In the road.

THE VASTEST THINGS ARE
THOSE WE MAY NOT LEARN

Mervyn Peake

The vastest things are those we may not learn.
We are not taught to die, nor to be born,
Nor how to burn
With love.
How pitiful is our enforced return
To those small things we are the masters of.

sleeping naked in a bed of poppies
with a bottle tucked under my arm

what's right & what's necessary don't usually stride
merrily along hand in hand. they rarely coincide, as
much as they collide. sometimes it's impossible to
find a common ground between flying & falling.

we can innocently assume the wrong position, be
it missionary, crucifixion or upside down. we can get
nailed with a stereotype that doesn't resemble us in
the least. we can find ourselves decked out in a
hairshirt that's all the rage, but doesn't fit. we can be
reduced to the latest example, a martyr in the cross-
fire, or find ourselves in a different circle-where
precision is another word for deliberate miss & a
zero is more intimidating than a thick red line.

sometimes it takes a good night's sleep in a bed of
poppies to dream up a straight story. sometimes it
takes a profane stream of consciousness to wipe
out the blasphemy of silence. sometimes it takes
years of lining them up & knocking them back to
see there's no established order. sometimes it takes
running naked & screaming, to strip away definitions
& comprehend the beauty of in other words.

mark hartenbach 2005

from **AUTOBIOGRAPHY OF A SMALL, MEAN MAN (I)**

by Richard Hell.

I keep trying to find ways to make
myself attractive in my poems. I mean
really attractive, more attractive than anyone else.
After all, it ought to be possible--I don't have to answer
questions afterwards, nobody can see me
while they're reading them, I have all of literature
to steal from, etc., etc. Still, I
can't seem to do it--it's partly because I'm
lazy (he brags, insinuating), but also because the moment I
succeed in giving the impression I possess
some appealing quality, I've deprived myself
of variations on it and that drives me
crazy, plus there're all the existing poems
with such strong claims to intelligence,
insight, sensitivity, wit, etc., etc., that
since they are my models, how can I
possibly surpass them? The thing that really
worries me though is that I'm afraid
that hardly anyone but me is actually
drawn towards the traits I've tried so hard
to suggest belong to the author of the poems I sign.
That is really scary. It would mean my life is
wasted twice. Doubly wasted. Can you top that?

For a Dead Lady

E A Robinson

No more with overflowing light
Shall fill the eyes that now are faded,
Nor shall another's fringe with night
Their woman-hidden world as they did.
No more shall quiver down the days
The flowing wonder of her ways,
Whereof no language may requite
The shifting and the many-shaded.

The grace, divine, definitive,
Clings only as a faint forestalling;
The laugh that love could not forgive
Is hushed, and answers to no calling;
The forehead and the little ears
Have gone where Saturn keeps the years;
The breast where roses could not live
Has done with rising and with falling.

The beauty, shattered by the laws
That have creation in their keeping,
No longer trembles at applause,
Or over children that are sleeping;
And we who delve in beauty's lore
Know all that we have known before
Of what inexorable cause
Makes Time so vicious in his reaping.

UNEXPRESSED

Paul
Laurence
Dunbar (1872-1906)

DEEP in my heart that aches with the
repression,
And strives with plenitude of bitter pain,
There lives a thought that clamors for
expression,
And spends its undelivered force in vain.

What boots it that some other may have
thought it?
The right of thoughts' expression is divine;
The price of pain I pay for it has bought it,
I care not who lays claim to it -- 't is mine!

And yet not mine until it be delivered;
The manner of its birth shall prove the test.
Alas, alas, my rock of pride is shivered -
I beat my brow -- the thought still
unexpressed.

Letter to modzine ALL OR NOTHING from March 1987:

Dear Lee,

Just dropping you a line after reading issue 3 of All or Nothing, because you're always complaining that no one can be bothered to write to you.

I thought the Steve Marriott interview was the best thing I've read in a modzine for ages, and I was very interested to read your views on the state of Mod.

I totally agree with you. More and more I ask myself what has happened to suits and even ties no longer seem to be favoured.

But it's not only dress that seems to have gone downhill, I have noticed a lack (an extreme one at that) of cool behaviour in our clubs. No longer do some modernists (the majority unfortunately) worry about acting cool, instead they jump around like idiots. It has got very bad recently, though i don't know if Christmas and New year were to blame, they shouldn't be.

The 'Rolf Harris' [a Mod scooter club] seem to have pioneered this uncool explosion, what can

you expect from people who are seen in t-shirts
and jeans? but sadly they are no longer alone,
in fact it seems to be the in thing to act
silly.

Surely the whole idea of modernism is to act
hip as well as dress hip! That's what I've
thought anyhow, am I wrong?

As for poseing it is nonexistant in 1987, these
uncool dudes just lounge around when they're not
fooling around. Fortunately I am not alone in
this opinion but we seem to be a small group. I
sincerely hope that we can return to being the
smartly dressed, cool, well mannered elite that
our predecessors were in the late 50's/early
60's. I'm not saying that everybody has to
dress like me or share my musical preferences
only that as Modernists we should have some
dignity, Ya dig?

Stay Cool,
A.S.
(Amphetimine Anonymous)

Paul Laurence Dunbar
(1872-1906)

We Wear the Mask

We wear the mask that grins and lies,
It hides our cheeks and shades our eyes,--
This debt we pay to human guile;
With torn and bleeding hearts we smile,
And mouth with myriad subtleties.

Why should the world be overwise,
In counting all our tears and sighs?
Nay, let them only see us, while
We wear the mask.

We smile, but, O great Christ, our cries
To thee from tortured souls arise.
We sing, but oh the clay is vile
Beneath our feet, and long the mile;
But let the world dream otherwise,
We wear the mask!

Give me leave to rail at you

by John Wilmot

Give me leave to rail at you, -
I ask nothing but my due:
To call you false, and then to say
You shall not keep my heart a day.
But alas! against my will
I must be your captive still.
Ah! be kinder, then, for I
Cannot change, and would not die.
Kindness has resistless charms;
All besides but weakly move;
Fiercest anger it disarms,
And clips the wings of flying love.
Beauty does the heart invade,
Kindness only can persuade;
It gilds the lover's servile chain,
And makes the slave grow pleased again.

How To Get Laid

James Lineberger

Tell her that sex
always makes you feel lonely
and afraid and afterwards

you usually have to get up and eat a peanut
butter sandwich and watch
Letterman

Tell her that when you were
at the Guthrie
you had a half a Ford Grant and a half

a Rockefeller

Tell her that your favorite actress
is Margaret Lockwood

Tell her that you know Gregory
Corso

Tell her that the last time you made love for
real it was with
a woman who couldn't get off

unless she was wearing headphoness
listening
to Brian Wilson

Tell her you think you're losing your grip
Tell her you don't know which way to turn
Tell her you're crazy

about the little hairs on her arms

Tell her you're not worth
saving

Tell her you know Sam Shephard
Tell her you're just lost
Tell her your favorite actress is Veronica Lake

Tell her you've never been to Kilamanjaro

but you have seen
the northern lights over the St. Lawrence and how
Quebec

falls straight off into the water

Tell her you are visited by spirits who have no voices
and require
you to read their lips leading

to situations in which
like Warhol
like Nixon like Esther Williams you have often

but slenderly known yourself

Tell her that Gregory Corso is the only poet of your
acquaintance (except maybe Bill
Harmon) that would ever dare to come up with a word

Like *brool*

Tell her that Jane Fonda has really strong
hands and once massaged

your back like Hayden wasn't home like you could ask
her
anything

Tell her she can ask you anything
Tell her there are some things you simply can't talk
about

Tell her
that Sam Shephard's work is like a
like a

like one of these people that lays on the beach too long
at Santa Monica
and gets loopy from the fumes

Tell her when you lived at Steele Creek your mama had
a terrier name of Sam
that she used to shove up into the attic every

night to hunt for rats

Tell her you not only know the man who wrote *Tubby
the Tuba* but have heard
him play his own composition

Tell her does
she dream in color or black and white

Tell her that when you were at the Chelsea
they gave you the room
where Thomas Wolfe had stayed and you couldn't

write a single line
the entire time you were there but at least

you got to meet
Gregory Corso who prowled
the halls a lot
and once borrowed your felt-tip to scribble

brool
in cursive on the marble steps

Tell her *oh God*
how it finally happened that you ended up just
like your father

broke and busted in the wilds of Burbank
nowhere to turn not
an orange grove in sight

fighting with this old woman behind the Kentucky Fried
to decide
which one of you would get the chance to pick

through the leavings in the dumpster

how you got the woman down and tried
to strangle her
smelled her fear felt the loose

flesh under her arms
tasted the spittle trailing down her cheek

how all of a sudden it wasn't an old woman at all

it was Jane Fonda saying
don't kill me don't we can take turns

Tell her

you knew Allen Tate in the sixties
and Allen Tate's semi-

spick wife who was about a hundred years old
and never failed
to introduce herself as a Yale

Younger Poet

Tell her that your favorite actress in the whole entire
world
is this French woman
that fell in love with a German soldier

in *Hiroshima Mon Amour*
and when the people in her village found out about it
they cut off

all her hair
and then after the war she was with this Japanese
guy and so she had to tell

the truth didn't she so
she told him everything and the ashes rained
all over them

Tell her to quit
looking at you like that

Tell her
that much as you hate to admit it Jorie Graham
is probably the best poet around
and a person you lust after day and night

and once wrote a letter to requesting her autograph

or one of her bras
Tell her tell her
you have to tell her something:
Tell her
it's happening it's love at first sight

Tell her you know she feels the same way
Tell her
you can read her every thought

but she may as well
get one thing straight: you wouldn't even
let Constance Ockleman
fuck you on a first date

SIXTEEN

Marie Kazalia

older teenage boys with cars
pick me & my girlfriends up at the Dairy Freeze
end of our shift
giving us a ride home, they say
but instead drive along back country roads
they have beer but I don't drink any
park near some old abandoned buildings
near grassy railroad tracks
I don't know where the other girls have gone
with the other boys in the pouring rainstorm
I stand under the overhang
above an old wooden loading dock
rain funneling the force of water
through a big overhead drain pipe
step under it—wash away summer heat and sweat
unceasing gush rinses the chocolate syrup stains
from the front of my white Dairy Freeze uniform
soaking wet—hair clinging to my head
uniform presses teenage breasts in wet bra
soaking panties visible through synthetic white—
I'm so virginally desire-less
not understanding how sexy
—yet somehow knowing and embarrassed—
the teenage boy watching from the ground below
frozen mouth gaping for several moments
as I scream laughing in the cool gushing rain water

Never shit on your own doorstep

Danny McCosh.

When Frederico got home
Maria was waiting up for him,
He'd been doing her punters and she was not happy.
She ripped his face and tore his hair,
He grabbed a knife
So did she,
They glared at each other across the kitchen table,
The first one to sleep dies,' said he.
Fortunately they had loads of enemies
And just at that moment
Someone threw a brick through the window
This diffused the situation somewhat.

CLEANING PLANET ASSHOLE
By Daniel Joshua Nagelberg

Bums lie dead
Like beached
Walruses
On this vomit-drenched
Island
In the middle
Of the city

Putting cigarettes
Out
In puddles of

Still-moist
Wretch
We are the
Clean-up crew

We harpoon the
Carcasses and
Toss them into
The shredder
Liquefying them
Recycling
Both
Their bodies
And
Final thoughts
Turning them
Into lager
Vodka
Booze
That gets
Poured back
Down the
Throats
Of idiots
In search of
The great party

The party is
A mass murder
A gang rape
Blood
On the white collar

A thousand
Fist fights
Furious
Self-disappointment
Depression
Pass-outs
Hand-ins
Suicides

The crew
Does not wonder
Why we never have
A day off

SOMETIME DURING ETERNITY

Lawrence Ferlinghetti (1958)

Sometime during eternity
some guys show up
and one of them
who shows up real late
is a kind of carpenter
from some square-type place
like Galilee
and he starts wailing
and claiming he is hep
to who made heaven
and earth
and that the cat
who really laid it on us
is his Dad

And moreover
he adds
It's all writ down
on some scroll-type parchments
which some henchmen
leave lying around the Dead Sea somewheres
a long time ago
and which you won't even find
for a coupla thousand years or so
or at least for
nineteen hundred and fortyseven
of them
to be exact
and even then
nobody really believes them
or me

for that matter

You're hot
they tell him

And they cool him

They stretch him on the Tree to cool
And everybody after that
is always making models
of this Tree
with Him hung up
and always crooning His name
and calling Him to come down
and sit in
on their combo
as if he is THE king cat
who's got to blow
or they can't quite make it

Only he don't come down
from His Tree

Him just hang there
on His Tree
looking real Petered out
and real cool
and also
according to a roundup
of late world news
from the usual unreliable sources
real dead

BALLAD OF THE SAD YOUNG MEN

Fran Landesman

Sing a song of sad young men
Glasses full of rye
All the news is bad again
Kiss your dreams goodbye

All the sad young men
Sitting in the bars
Knowing neon nights
Missing all the stars

All the sad young men
Drifting through the town
Drinking up the night
Trying not to drown

All the sad young men
Singing in the cold
Trying to forget
That they're growing old

All the sad young men
Choking on their youth
Trying to be brave
Running from the truth

Autumm turns the leaves to gold
Slowly dies the heart
Sad young men are growing old
That's the cruelest part

All the sad young men
seek a certain smile
Someone they can hold
for a little while
Tired little girl does the best she can
Trying to be gay for a sad young man

While the grimy moon
Watches from above
All the sad young men
Play at making love

Misbegotten moon
Shine for sad young men
Let your gentle light
Guide them home tonight

All the sad young men

Late-Flowering Lust

Sir John Betjeman

My head is bald, my breath is bad,
  Unshaven is my chin,
I have not now the joys I had
  When I was young in sin.

I run my fingers down your dress
  With brandy-certain aim
And you respond to my caress
  And maybe feel the same.

But I've a picture of my own
  On this reunion night,
Wherein two skeletons are shewn
  To hold each other tight;

Dark sockets look on emptiness
  Which once was loving-eyed,
The mouth that opens for a kiss
  Has got no tongue inside.

I cling to you inflamed with fear
  As now you cling to me,
I feel how frail you are my dear
  And wonder what will be—

A week? or twenty years remain?
  And then—what kind of death?
A losing fight with frightful pain
  Or a gasping fight for breath?

Too long we let our bodies cling,
  We cannot hide disgust
At all the thoughts that in us spring
  from this late-flowering lust.

GOD WORKS IN MYSTERIOUS WAYS

by Paul Birtill.

Aberfan, Multiple Sclerosis
Spastics and the Somme
Bloody Mysterious…

Cancer, Culloden
Famine and President Botha
Weird…

Motorway pile-ups
Cot-deaths and Hiroshima
A trifle peculiar…

Schizophrenia, Zeebrugge
Thatcherism and Belsen
Damn strange…

Aids and Ulster
Strokes, Cardboard City
and of course the
Human being

Is he worth an hour
on Sunday{?}
Surely not…

CHOICES

Nikki Giovanni.

if i can't do
what i want to do
then my job is to not
do what i don't want
to do

it's not the same thing
but it's the best i can
do

if i can't have
what i want . . . then
my job is to want
what i've got
and be satisfied

that at least there
is something more to want

since i can't go
where i need
to go . . . then i must . . . go
where the signs point
through always understanding
parallel movement
isn't lateral

when i can't express
what i really feel
i practice feeling
what i can express
and none of it is equal
i know
but that's why mankind
alone among the animals
learns to cry

MOTTO

Bertholt Brecht

In the dark times
Will there also be singing?
Yes, there will be singing
About the dark times.

PAM AYRES LOSES IT ON HER COMEBACK

by The Pam Ayres Appreciation Society

Allergic
Largactil
Till death do us part
I stepped on a duck
And it uttered a fart
I freeform this rhyme.
And proclaim it
as Art,

Like a siren,
I garner
No reviews from the south.
I once had a comeback
And it sealed
Shut my mouth.

Extract from *The Prettiest Star*

Nina Antonia

Family life, the other great facade, also exploded albeit internally. Adultery sounded like pottery or cookery to me, something that one took as an evening class. Did adulterers get top marks for cheating? Half in love with the drama of infidelity Wanda had grown careless in her affair with Rodney Curtis and neglected the conditions of her pedestal.

Eventually Howard employed a detective to kep tabs on her. I knew something was wrong the day I returned home from school and saw my father's car parked in the drive. He rarely got in this early. I found him in the lounge drinking copious amounts of whisky and listening to a wretched Elvis Presley number called 'My Boy'. Sorrow had affected his normally good taste. He kept playing the song over and over again. Early Presley was okay, but 'My Boy' was sheer Vegas slush, a divorced father's lament to his only son, with the repeated refrain:

'You're all I have my boy, my life, my pride, my joy.'

I wanted to scream "What about me?"

But instead I went upstairs to listen to the New York Dolls.

Be Nowhere Now

WHITMAN McGOWAN

Create a plan for yourself, then abandon it.
Whine about not being able to realize your potential.
Outline details of stumbling blocks to confidants.
Spend all your spare time escaping.
Drink, travel, and talk about writing potboilers perhaps.
Sleep until noon, then go around in a daze. Be nowhere now.

Go online.
Browse hundreds of pages of magazine like sites
whilst never leaving the comfort of your swivel chair
or taking off your heads up wireless internet display. Follow the
market.
Get swept up in waves of elation & fear.
Hold stock in companies whose leaders you despise. Be nowhere
now.

Wear clean looking conformist fashion
the duds to make you look successful.
Sell yourself as something you're not, except for money.
Make a list of specifications of prospective dates.
Create a series of fantastical ideal relationships.
Approach love like a remodeling project. Be nowhere now.

Operate intensely within your own increasingly narrow sphere.
Cultivate people you can exploit or suck up to.
Try to look responsible when it comes to family life
but drop the pretense of having any ideals.
Hire a better lawyer than your lame adversary.
Mock anybody else's claim to righteousness. Be nowhere now.

Eat prepared food you cook in a microwave
instant meals containing God knows what from God knows where.
Say, smacking your lips, these are pretty good.
Sign up for a huge Millennium party
even though you can't afford it and it's not the Millennium
and the fireworks and the music will probably be forgettable.
Be nowhere now.

Buy a four wheel drive SUV
and park it in the city
making you look like the outdoors type.
Get a cellular and start walking and talking.
Don't be noticing what's around you
because you can be anywhere else in your so called mind.
Be nowhere now.

Extra Long Pink Hose

Whitman McGowan

I have to thank my property manager
for this new extra long pink hose he bought us.
Twice as long as the last one
pink and ever so firm when gorged with fluid
my new extra long pink hose enables me
to service my entire building and my neighbors as well.
With it I make the friendly young black motel worker happy
and the old hippie caretaker for the condo building, he likes it, too.
After a dry spell or after a rainy day
whenever there's lots of street trash around
my new extra long pink hose can service an entire block.

When I got it out and squirted on the sidewalk
only a couple of people said anything like, What a waste!
or, Where I come from, we can't spare a drop.
But I haven't been arrested yet for using it in public.

My new extra long pink hose
makes a difference in everybody's life.
There are only a couple of problems with it.
First, it's very long and heavy.
I get tired holding it
and before I walk to the other end
I have a habit of dropping it
and the head whips around and drenches me so
I am beside myself with emotion
making it difficult to turn myself off.

Also, it doesn't dribble like an old hose
but as long there's no kink in my extra long pink hose
it has a tendency to spurt uncontrollably
when a pretty woman walks by smiling at me.
And I don't want to get all the women wet
in my neighborhood, now do I?

<u>Why superstition must be maintained</u>
by Graham Martin

A ladder in the street,
And understood
by all people's feet,
who walk around,
obey the lore,
Except one young buck,
a useless tit, who walks right through,
the little shit!

Has lucky escape,
and mocks superstition,
And watching, I have a nasty vision.

An idea comes,
I throw a can
right at the head of this young man,
a perfect aim,
His cranium!
He's buried now
beneath
some
geranium.

Layin' Up With Linda

GG Allin

Layin' up with Linda
Use to be fun
Nobody ever paid the rent
There was never anything done
And then one day I killed her
Now I'm on the run
But livin' with Linda
Use to be fun

Livin' with Linda
She did what I wanted her to do
But livin' with Linda
Wasn't always easy to do
So one day I killed her
Now I'm on the run
But livin' with Linda
Use to be fun

Layin' up with Linda
Never had responsibility
She was a dancer at night
I was rock 'n' rolling 'til three
We drank, we never saw the daylight
That was the death of her and me
And one day I just got bored and killed her
But she use to be fun

Layin' up with Linda
We stole, we fought, we fucked

Never had a quarter
Everything we owned was in hock
Then I got pissed and killed her
So now I'm on the run
But I'll tell ya livin' with Linda
Use to be fun

Words and Music by GG Allin
recorded by GG Allin & The Carolina Shitkickers
(1993)

Be Drunk

Baudelaire

You have to be always drunk. That's all there is to it—it's the only way. So as not to feel the horrible burden of time that breaks your back and bends you to the earth, you have to be continually drunk.

But on what? Wine, poetry or virtue, as you wish. But be drunk.

And if sometimes, on the steps of a palace or the green grass of a ditch, in the mournful solitude of your room, you wake again, drunkenness already diminishing or gone, ask the wind, the wave, the star, the bird, the clock, everything that is flying, everything that is groaning, everything that is rolling, everything that is singing, everything that is speaking. . .ask what time it is and wind, wave, star, bird, clock will answer you: "It is time to be drunk! So as not to be the martyred slaves of time, be drunk, be continually drunk! On wine, on poetry or on virtue as you wish."

Anti-Slavery Movements

Benjamin Zephaniah

Some people say
Animal liberators are not
Working in the interest of animals.
But I've never seen liberated animals
Protest by going back to their place
Of captivity.
But then again
I've never heard of any liberated slaves
Begging for more humiliation
Or voting for slavery.

Animals vote with their feet
Or their wings
Or their fins.

Egocentric

by Stevie Smith

What care I if good God be
If he be not good to me,
If he will not hear my cry
Nor heed my melancholy midnight sigh?
What care I if he created Lamb,
And Golden Lion, and mud-delighting Clam,

And Tiger stepping out on padded toe,
And the fecund earth the blindworms know?
He made the Sun, the Moon and every Star,
He made the infant Owl and the Baboon,
He made the ruby-orbed Pelican,

He made all silent inhumanity,
Nescient and quiescent to his will,

Unquickened by the questing conscious flame,
That is my glory and my bitter bane.
What care I if skies are blue,
If God created Gnat and Gnu,
What care I if good God be
If he be not good to me?

INTIMATES

by D H Lawrence

Don't you care for my love? She said bitterly

I handed her the mirror, and said:
Please address these questions to
the proper person!

Please make all requests to headquarters!
In all matters of emotional importance
please approach the supreme
authority direct! -
- So I handed her the mirror.

And she would have broken it over my head,
but she caught sight of her
own reflection
and that held her spellbound for two seconds
while I fled.

DADDY

Sylvia Plath

You do not do, you do not do
Any more, black shoe
In which I have lived like a foot
For thirty years, poor and white,
Barely daring to breathe or Achoo.

Daddy, I have had to kill you.
You died before I had time -
Marble-heavy, a bag full of God,
Ghastly statue with one gray toe
Big as a frisco seal

And a head in the freakish Atlantic
Where it pours bean green over blue
In the waters off beautiful Nauset.
I used to pray to recover you.
Ach, du.

In the German tongue, in the Polish town
Scraped flat by the roller
Of wars, wars, wars.
But the name of the town is common.
My Polack friend

Says there are a dozen or two.
So I never could tell where you
Put your foot, your root,
I never could talk to you.
The tongue stuck in my jaw.

It stuck in a barbed wire snare.
Ich, ich, ich, ich,
I could hardly speak.
I thought every German was you.
And the language obscene

An engine, an engine
Chuffing me off like a jew.
A Jew to Dachau, Auschwitz, Belsen.
I began to talk like a Jew.
I think I may well be a Jew.

The snows of the Tyrol, the clear beer of Vienna
Are not very pure or true.
With my gipsy ancestress and my weird luck.
And my Taroc pack and my Taroc pack
I may be a bit of a Jew.

I have always been scared of *you*,
With your luftwaffe, your gobbledygoo.
And your neat mustache
And your Aryan eye, bright blue.
Panzer-man, panzer-man, O You -

Not God but a swastika
So black no sky could squeak through.
Every woman adores a fascist,
The boot in the face, the brute
Brute heart of a brute like you.

You stand at the blackboard, daddy,
In the picture I have of you,
A cleft in your chin instead of your foot
But no less a devil for that, no not
Any less the black man who

Bit my pretty red heart in two.
I was ten when they buried you.
At twenty I tried to die
And get back, back, back to you.
I thought even the bones would do.

But they pulled me out of the sack,
And they stuck me together with glue.
And then I knew what to do.
I made a model of you,
A man in black with a Meinkampf look

And a love of the rack and the screw.
And I said I do , I do.
So daddy, I'm finally through.
The black telephone's off at the root,
The voices just can't worm through.

If I've killed one man, I've killed two -
The vampire who said he was you
And drank my blood for a year,
Seven years, if you want to know.
Daddy, you can lie back now.

There's a stake in your fat black heart
And the villagers never liked you.
They are dancing and stamping on you.
They always *knew* it was you.
Daddy, daddy, you bastard, I'm through.

Sylvia Plath (1962)

Pain Reliever

Eric Bogosian

Hi! Like most people I have the kind of job that stresses me out twenty-four-seven/three-sixty-five. And after five cups of coffee. I get a headache that feels like someone's driving nails into my skull with a sledgehammer. I used to think there was nothing I could do. I tried aspirin, Tylenol, Excedrin, even Extra Strength Advil—nothing worked. I'd writhe in agony at my desk all day and lie awake all night. That was before I discovered something that works better, lasts longer and lets me get the rest I need so I wake up refreshed in the morning ready to hit that traffic jam—heroin. Taken daily, heroin gets rid of my headaches like *no other* pain reliever. Ten milligrams in the morning, ten milligrams at night and my pain is *gone*. Heroin—the modern pain reliever. *(New, snappier voice) And next time, instead of those five cups of coffee, try crack - the quicker picker-upper.*

Winter in
The City of Friendship
by Mary Karr

Friend, some nights when I smoke on the fire escape,
I search beyond the snow-plowed streets
to the cold blue light of the study
in the tower in which you've walled yourself,
surrounded by minions and the books
that bolster your arguments.

Who will question you in this place?
You exile those who question, and your eyes,
which sometimes wheel this way
like searchlights do not make me out,
but cast the bright interior
shape of your face across mine.
Over and over, you erase me this way.

Still, I know the last kind word
that passed between us must circle
your tower. A small white bird,
it pecks your sill, songless,
its heart thrumming dimly.
It will not leave you,
however heavy the shade you draw,
however broad the back you turn.
It taps the frosted glass with a sound
like tiny iron letters embossed
against parchment, keys pressed
by fingers on a hand you refuse
to reach for, however much alone.

BLUES

Edward Kamau Braithwaite

i wake up this mornin'
sunshine int showin' through my door
i wake up this mornin'
sunshine int showin' through my door
'cause the blues is got me
and I int got strength to go no more

I wake up this mornin'
clothes still scattered 'cross the floor
i wake up this mornin'
clothes still scattered 'cross the floor
las' night the ride was lovely
but she int comin' back for more

sea island sunshine
where are you hidin' now
sea island sunshine
where are you hidin' now
could'a sware i left you in the cupboard
but is only empties mockin' at me in there now

empty bottles knockin'
laugh like a woman satisfied
empty bottles knockin'
laugh like a woman satisfied
she full an' left me empty
laughin' when i should'a cried

this place is empty bottles
this place is a woman satisfied

this place is empty bottles
this place is a woman satisfied
she drink muh sugar water
till muh sunshine died

i wake up this mornin'
sunshine int showin' through my door
i wake up this mornin'
sunshine int showin' through my door
she gone an' left me empty
and i should'a died…

LETTER TO ANDRE BRETON
(excerpt)

By Antonin Artaud

About the 28th of February, 1947

Dear friend,

You bitterly reproached me for my performance at the Vieux-Columbier which was the first occasion that I had found to tell the public of this society what I thought of them,

a society which had kept me interned for 9 years,

my spinal column demolished by their police with blows from iron bars,

the pimps struck me twice in the back with knives,

arrested and sent to prison, deported,

attacked on a boat,

kept secretly for 3 years during my first 3 years of internment,

Systematically poisoned during 5 months in one of their insane asylums (that of Sotteville-lès-Rouen, October 1937 - March 1938).

Perhaps I did get people in a theatre to make my accusation,

but to say that I remain a man of the theatre, as you say I do in your letter, by the mere fact that I appeared on stage,

is a gratuitous injustice

for I do not believe, no matter what boasting there might be in saying it, that any man of the theatre since the theatre has existed had adapted before me the attitude that I had that night on the stage of the Vieux-Columbier, and which consisted of belling on stage hateful eructations, colics and cramps to the extent of a syncope etc., etc.

Outside of gathering people in a theatre,

it also remained for me to castigate this society in the street,

but it's difficult for the streets are filled only with hurrying passerbys, and to invite them to listen one needs barricades and bombs,

but how is it that you did not *notice* that on stage at Vieux-Columbier I myself realized the inanity of my attempt and giving up the idea of reading the talk that I prepared I packed my bags and *left*, hurling into the public the last stanza of a poem:

> All the yoga exercises
> Are not worth the desquamations
> From the cunt of a dead nunch
> When the wench who spreads it
> Pisses while quartering her udder
> In order to cross syphilis

for I suddenly realized that the hour had passed to gather people in a theatre *even* to tell them truths and that with society and its public there is no longer a language other than that of bombs, machineguns, barricades and all that follows.

But how after that, André Breton, and after having reproached me for appearing in a theatre, can you invite me to participate in an exhibition, in an art gallery, hyper-chic, ultra-flourishing, loud, capitalistic (even if it had its funds in a communist bank) and where all demonstration can only have now the stylized, limited, closed, fixed character of a tentative art.

In a gallery one sells Painting, one buys paintings, it's a counter like the Jesuit counters in India or that of Lally-Tollendal, the objects on display are put in a box (in a coffin) or in show-windows, in incubators, that's no longer life;

all the snobs meet there like, alas! at the Orangerie they met before Van Gogh who deserved a much different night.

For there is nothing that brings down to earth the cosmog-

raphy, the hydrography, the demography, the science of eclipses, of the equinoxes and the seasons as does a painting by Van Gogh.

No, I can absolutely not participate in an exhibition, and especially in a gallery,

…..

THE BEST TIME OF DAY

by June Hird

In all our years together the only subject about which you and I disagreed was the best time of the day. As I snuggled into your arms at night I would say "evening", knowing that you and I were together, safe and warm until morning.

As I drowsily awoke, the delicious aroma of freshly-made coffee and hot buttered toast teased my taste-buds. Your smiling newly-shaved face materialising to my half-closed eye-lids. A kiss and a whiff of your aftershave and "wakey wake, a new day awaits us".

Even on holiday after dancing until the wee small hours you would still be up at day-break eager to seek pastures new.

That last morning I made the toast and coffee for you. You were eating breakfast as I made some coffee for myself. When I came to join you, you had gone, half of the warm coffee still in the cup.

He will not come back, they said but I could not believe them. Your electric razor still plugged in. Your smart new clothes still hanging in place.

You could not leave like that, so many plans still unfulfilled.

I only know that without you there is no best time of day.

Oh America

Penny Rimbaud

Not like the brazen giant of Greek fame
with conquering limbs astride from land to land,
there, at those sea-washed sunset gates, stands
a mighty woman with a torch, whose flame
Is imprisoned lightning.
And her name? Liberty, Mother of Exiles.

'Oh, America,' cries she with silent lips,
'give me the ghosts of people who you destroyed and whose Nation you
stole, that I might learn their ancient wisdom and be shown a pathway
to solace.
Give me the spirits of those who across dark seas you shipped here
in shackles, that the bondage of history might be destroyed and they
reunited with their forefathers.
Give me land of free tenure, free of enclosure, land undefiled by cupid-
ity's clasping claws, nor fire scorched by your endless wars;
a place where place has not been usurped.
Give me a simple home which is not a rich man's castle, which is not a
defence against life, but a confirmation of life itself; give me a roof that
will shelter love rather than protect avarice.
Give me oceans which are not hunting grounds, continents which are
not killing fields.
Give me air unpolluted by the smokestacks of unbridled commerce,
water untainted by your saccharine duplicity.
Give me food which is the fruit of honest labour rather than the curse of
abject slavery.
Give me a bed which celebrates free-thinking joy rather than callow
lasciviousness.

Give me love which is not ersatz, which is not a prostitution, which is not perverted by your Hollywood heist.

Give me your bodies free of vanity, bodies which are not silicone, not the crude patchwork of the surgeon's knife, nor shrouded by the purdah of tawdry fashion. Cast off the obesity of Narcissus that I might once see you naked and proud.

Give me a dream, but not your dream,

for first you must rewrite it.

Oh, America, do you not see? As those tragic towers toppled to your homicidal connivance, liquid assets oozed like black gold from your vaults, ran in dark streams from your marbled emporiums, past helpless security guards disarmed in their confusion, and out onto the cinder-caked streets. Tossing aside the theatre of sorrow, reptilian shoals of cocaine-driven brokers, Prozac-popping investors and Valium-blind shareholders rushed forward to consider possible gain through the consolidation of loss: Ground Zero. Who really questioned from whence the storm had blown? Three thousand martyrs for the cause of oil. Who really cared? Yet even before the burnt offering to Mammon, the terrible vengeance that could be wrought in its name had been contrived by those who breathed the noxious breath of intrigue. Democracy's whores were free at last to unleash the ghoul of hegemony that for so long they had been nurturing: a war that will last a lifetime - Afghanistan, Iraq, Iran, Syria, North Korea: the list is endless, the message is clear. But, Lord, dear Lord, how many lifetimes do we have? And as the planet is bludgeoned into cowering submission, and innocents are slaughtered in their thousands, corpulent corporate tycoons will be aided from the clammy leather back-seats of over-stretched limos to be led to illicit private bookings. They'll puff on cigars as big as their biggest phallic fantasies, salivate over very special menus, feed their dyspepsia and belch, rank on usury, while speculating on the rise and fall of their pubescent escorts' cleavages and the rock-solid investments that hang between them. Oh

yes, diamonds are a girl's best friend, a wife's worst enemy, and a flesh-tearing manacle to the poor wretches forced to scrape them free from the earth. Sated by excess, and an obsession with possession which now threatens to smother even their innate ignorance, the tired tycoons will clench their fat arses, and reach-out their porky hands towards their torpid escorts' powdered flesh, seeking to leech from it a life-blood that in all their crumpled decadence they have never known. And in the pitiful self-delusion of this hedonistic hell, the neon will flash and the billboards bray, and through the damnable pall of war the catch-phrase will remain the same: 'if you're not with us, you're against us - consume'. And in their self-imposed impotence, the crowds will be eager to oblige. The old world of cheese-cake security has been unceremoniously binned, but the new world will be giftwrapped. Garish gadgets and geegaws, trifling trinkets and trash: the cluster bombs of consumerism. Money changes hands, but always ends up in the same pockets. Friend or foe, what's it matter? You only live once; that much now seems painfully conclusive. The essence is simple, Ground Zero is the post-modernist symbol of capitalism, the heart and soul, the sordid justification. There's no option now but to dive deeper into the belly of the ravaged beast. Don't think: buy. Don't stop: spend. Prove to yourself that you still exist. Ciao, bambino. Buy, buy.

Oh, America, give me values free of your ticker-tape psychosis, free of jingoistic prattle, free of your terrible mission.
Give me justice which is not the searing spite of your revenge.
Give me peace which is not the product of war, nor dependent on it.
Give me hope where there is only despair, a future which is not your loathsome crusade.
Give me freedom where now there is only servitude.
Give me face where facelessness has become the norm.
Give me music which feeds from the soul rather than stealing from it.
Give me time which is not measured by the scourge of your

deadly dollar.

Give me the honesty of considered reason rather than the cheap escape of glib rationalisation.

Give me those who truly sung your praises yet whose heritage you now defile - Whitman, Steinbeck, Ginsberg, Pollock and Rothko, Ayler and Coltrane - that they might sing again of a love supreme.

Give me your philosophers that we might fly high together above the cuckoo's nest of your insanity.

Give me the madmen, the outsiders, the hustlers and the beats who you so decry,

then give me your own tired, your own poor, your own huddled masses yearning to breathe free,

but give me also those from across the planet who you have enslaved with your cheap morality and your military might,

and we will wait.

Oh, America, give the homeless, tempest-tossed to me,
and we will cluster tight together and stand apart from you,
for until you heal yourself, I can offer none of these a home.

His Misery Unites Us.

Graham Martin.

A bloke,
on the bus,
in England football shirt,
spies a stumbling man in the street,

Addressing all six of us
on the bus,
in a sudden unity,
he draws our atttention to...
(through the bus window)
...the lugubrious man,
tight-lipped and pale,

"He's not smiling is he? Looks like he's had a skinful"

People reluctantly smile,
but want to be on side with the
bloke, see it like he does,
as he is a leader of men.

We all laugh a bit
(as if hypnotised by his brashness)
and try not to concede
that maybe the
aimless old man
isn't drunk at all.

There Is Some Bad Blood In The Joke Parlor

by Daniel Joshua Nagelberg

I was sitting at a small table in the back
Of the club
Had a good buzz flowing
There was one thing these people
And I had in common
We all wanted to laugh

I used to laugh at myself all the time
But honestly
I didn't find myself funny
Anymore

(Bass, snare, high-hat, thanks)

Two older ladies were
Sitting at a nearby table
Talking loudly about
Facelifts and ovaries
I wanted them to shut up
Actually
I wanted them dead

Finally the comedian
Came out
There was no introduction
He just kind of stumbled out
From behind the curtain
He was wearing a t-shirt
Which read
"The Giggle Saloon---Pasadena"

Tonight
I thought
I had better fucking
Laugh

"How's everyone doing tonight"
He asked
The audience produced the
Standard indistinguishable
Crowd noise then
Became silent

"Good, good," he said
Nervously
"Because I'm not doing so
Well"

His voice wavered
"Um, my wife was
Shot then raped today"

A few people laughed
I heard someone say
"Oh
God"
Yeah, did you all catch
The order?
Shot
Then
Raped"

The laughter became
Stronger

"In fact she's still out

In the middle of the street
Destroyed"

The stage light became
Slightly brighter and
His facial features
Were more defined
I could tell that he
Wasn't there
His body was
On that stage but
His brain was being
Encased in concrete
Denial

"Yeah and do you know
Who fucking did it?"

"WHO FUCKING DID IT?!?"
The crowd roared back

"Those fucking gorillas
Running for office,"
He screamed
"Those pro-wrestlers
Wearing the gasmasks
The spandex diapers
Wielding those fucking
Sledgehammers
Oh shit. . ."

He began whimpering
Into the microphone

While the audience laughed

Clapped and cheered
Three men wearing business suits
Were standing raising their
Beers and cheering each other

"Do you know what they said ?!?"
He screamed over the audience
Noise
"That they were going to thrust
Our cities into the ground
Like pencils through mud
If they don't get elected,"
He cried out
"Fucking great!"

One of the older ladies
Who was engaged in the
Facelift and ovary discussion
Began hysterically convulsing
While her friend just kept
Slapping the table and
Repeating
"This boy is funny shit"

"You stupid motherfuckers,"
He whined into the microphone
Then put his head down
As if defeated
He continued softly
"I walked over the bodies
Of three dead children
To get to this club
Tonight"

"Me too," a fat man

Yelled and stood up
Laughing
"But I ain't complaining,"

He pulled out two
Fifty-dollar bills and
Held them over his eyes
"I just wear a couple of
Presidents and dead
Kids magically disappear!"
He laughed a hearty and
Wheezy kind of laugh

The audience joined him
In his laughter and
Nodded to each other
Agreeing with his actions

The comedian
Ignoring the man
Continued
"And do you know
How all those psychotic convict
Wrestlers running for government
Came into this existence?"
"NO HOW DID THEY?!?"
The audience chanted
Simultaneously
"Let's just say that somebody
Cloned too many seedless watermelons
And one fucked-up fetus"

I had never seen anything
Like it

The laughter
The insanity
The men wearing their
Business suits all pulled
Out huge hunting knives
And began stabbing
Each other while laughing
Probably harder than
They had ever laughed before
I saw girlfriends beating
The shit out of their boyfriends
Throwing fists of laughter
One lonely man took himself by
The back of his head
Grabbed a handful of his own hair
And began slamming his
Head against a table
While spitting out his own
Blood and teeth
He was smiling
Ear to ear

"We're all going to die
Very shortly"
The comedian spoke softly
Into the microphone
I was probably the
Only one that heard him
I agreed
Quietly
To myself

Muffled in the hysterics
I heard organs being pierced
Skin being ripped like fabric

Bones breaking
Gunfire
A chainsaw
I snuck out a back
Exit and walked home
Barely amused

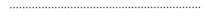

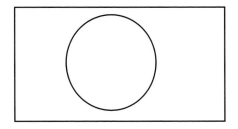

SUN
by
Mark Hartenbach

while still an adolescent
i buried the sun in the backyard
& when i need it most
i'll dig it up
many tell me i look vaguely familiar
but the name escapes them
maybe i have the best of both worlds
i'm the jumping hair in the newsreel
snaking its way into subconscious
serving no discernable purpose
except to rise
& fall

illumination poem
by
Mark Hartenbach

it was an illuminating experience
that began as disorientation
& ended up speechless

there were no witnesses
& i have nothing
to show for it

no enlightening explanation
or even
an interesting story

many stroke victims
lose the ability to speak
but can sing complete songs

the limitations
of rational thought & action
can be frustrating

we want to throw
everything we've written
into the fire

& watch
as art rises
from the ashes

From My Point of View
Steven Berkoff

'Of course I like the feeling of a full cunt,' she thought '.
. . I mean, who doesn't . . .and by full I mean choked full,
stuffed full, filled with meat and do I question, whose meat?
Yes, sometimes I can afford the luxury of discrimination and
yes I do like to be kissed occasionally and not just wham,
bam — put the kettle on love. I do like a man who's gentle
and considerate . . .kisses me tenderly and doesn't just ram
his hands up my skirt to his salvation, being a warm, wet,
receptacle for his seminal deposits. Yet how often, sitting in
my bed-sitting room do I get a call from someone I really
like, and yet more often than not, it's some Joe I met last
year failing in his little black book (his fuck directory well
thumbed) to find his usual bird clusters at home. Rings me —
a vaguely remembered bird he met in an equally vague party
or pub . . .and what the hell … "let's try this one," thinks he
… "Hallo, yes …who? …Joe who? …Oh!? … Well …OK,
I'll meet you in the …" usually some grotty pub he hangs out
in …not dinner, Oh no … "Thought we'd have a drink." He
splurges out on two large gins in the hope of. Should say no
really, hell rotten no! … But boredom mates uneasily with
loneliness producing an offspring unbeloved, called
desperation, fuck it …I brush my teeth to ameliorate my faggy
throat, change my tights and knickers (or maybe just my
knickers) fasten on my cap which I loathe wearing all the time
and head out. Thus equipped to face the world at large with
my plastic membrane holding back the anxious creatures the
monster lets loose from his bow …Still, I'm out …I'm in the

air …I'm using my voice and I see and smell …I'm paid attention to. I am bought …alright, so it's only a drink but I am bought it. I live like the rest of my human fraternity … smile, do I and act like I too belong the human race again, and not sitting on my bed wondering, as I stare at the walls of my prison sanctuary, wondering how I shall endure another bestial night …tormented by the sounds of music being played in the upstairs rooms and their voices laughing Oh so loudly …what can be so funny to make people laugh that loudly …I never remember laughing like that …what special ingredients fill their words and gestures to evoke such joy …perhaps it seems especially loud to me who am bathed in so much silence … sometimes I can't sleep (so inconsiderate they) and their laughter always tinkles on into the small hours …but it's lovely when there is silence again …then we are the same … our silence is shared by all …sitting there dreaming about kitchens with large wooden tables and chairs gathered round, cooking for my man's friends who come and chat idly, while I, pinafored, prepare … I like that …liberation? …I don't want liberating, I want imprisoning …suffocating in the arms of my man) I want him to ask me to make special things …I want him to *be* a bit late from the pub, what the hell, what's a half-hour or even an hour …you enjoy yourself darling …No I won't come to the pub I'd rather get the food ready and so I would, he's with me for life why hold back his separate precious hours, and I lay it out beautifully. My mother used to nag my father for tardiness of only ten minutes …lucky woman didn't know that to be alone and waiting for a man, any man, one might have to wait for years …never mind ten minutes, she didn't know how lucky she was. Poor dad

blustering in and chastised until his food wouldn't go down any more …until the chastisement so consumed him that he vomited out a thrombosis brought about through a heavy surfeit of nag, and then ma *had* him, really and truly had him all to herself …each day …every minute was hers … there he was upstairs, paralysed, in bed and whimpering for his cup of tea …and wasn't she solicitous then, but of course who has to stay home and work to support us, why I am the inheritor of that raging twisted mouth …or the deeds thereof since her venom's rewards fall to me …and who wants a bride of 40 when eventually he kicked it, poor dad, and I left home … hardly a virgin and barely anything …except…what could we do then, a girl of 20 and her boy-friend in the hall, standing up since sweet mum would hang around as if twisted for her own loss of male protuberance she therefore wished to share her empty hole with me or share her anguish … "don't be too long dear," she'd whine from the living room … "you've got work tomorrow," as if I didn't have work everyday and face the gloomy and drab departments of perpetual boredom and obligation … the poor guys in the cold hallway kissing me goodnight …with a sharp frottage against my taffeta (it was then and when it spun around in the dance hall it lifted like petals surrounding a stamen) fed up guys rubbing their hard passion against me in the passage way, while mother is straining her ears from the living room …and because it was a dark hallway and wretched ma calling, it made urgency for emission that more desperate, whereas a friendly cuddle on the couch and Billy Eckstein on the gramophone would have coaxed a more lasting appreciation …The hall was furtive, made dark for speed not relaxation, as if what cannot be

expressed in warmth and comfort but needs alleys and hallways, is something of a more dirty nature ...where the only demands are satisfaction ...so unknowingly but malevolently she condemned my young chances to dirt snatched and mangled ...wet pants and *no* love ...only their shuddering young bodies grabbing me ...their beards still soft ...their hips swivelling blindly against my mount of Venus ...and their poor throbbing hearts emptying their keen and youthful passion amidst sighs not unmixed with guilt for being condemned to alleyways, hallways and the dark recesses of tenements ... "Let's go up here love," he cajoles, at the inviting gloom of a staircase in some adjacent building smelling of cats and stale piss ... "It's OK love, it's dark ... please ...it's alright ... no one can see us ... please ..." Oh ...their young kisses sweeter than wine ...but they seldom came back ...I yielded too easily ...too hurt by my strained home, I wished to compensate, for that uncharitable guilt by giving them that, which in their young impetuous hearts they hoped I'd hold onto ...their burning silken pricks were desperate as so often I'd let their juices run onto my hand but their hearts grew rigid as their members softened ...as if my hand in their eyes was scummed for ever. They wanted a picture of something else, a picture of something that should have been more precious to me. They liked coming ...gasping and quivering in the final sun-burst of their lust but wanted the ache to last and not be assuaged that easily ... too easily. They pictured too many other bodies being satisfied against this mound of flesh and lavender water (I used then and sometimes still do) ...and while the race was their's that night and peaceful dreams their's, the hopes of continuance died as

if hope needs to be fed slowly for the thing one hopes for to have any real worth. "One must always struggle for something worthwhile in life," mother would simper …but why should I make them struggle …when I don't want them to. Perhaps I should force myself …they seldom phoned again and the years drifted by with a succession of young hard bodies and yards and yards of their white stiffened skin bursting in my hands like a crushed fruit …I became bolder …Did I care? No! and for what …the plague of parents, and of dad whom I truly did love, invests one at birth with such an awful magnitude of responsibility that one can't say no, and leave them to make do, can't leave home and make the nest I need to live …breathe and play Billy Eckstein …make coffee and gently dissuade their advances … for now anyway …win them gradually when trust grows from knowledge and affection and at least we could sit on the sofa and talk …I'll cook beautiful dinners …such whimpering idle romances drifted down like snow while some brute is fucking me under the staircase …stockings torn, knickers around my knees and he's fumbling to get it in deeper but my knees are trapped by my knickers and won't spread …he's cursing and pushing and hurting …Oh so shameless am I now …who cares now? … what honour do I have to protect? …No! I will not take my knickers off …I insist…shades of black comedy, I have my point of honour …On my knickers I make the last stand of respectability …my worn shreds of scruples …let them fuck me but I won't go out of my way to take my knickers off and stuff them in my handbag … "What am I, a whore?" …he laughs and heaving me up by the ass he affords himself a good position and I feel his jets squandering themselves in me

and he withdrawing almost as fast …no passion was extin-
guished quicker than this one. I stand …weakly in that black
staircase…my smells mingling with the odour of dustbins and
the vast effluvium that humanity discharges into them …so
much keener are the smells now after the act …and watch him
wiping his prick with a soiled crumpled handkerchief. "You
wanna borrow it love?" …his voice held just the faintest note
of compassion as if he too unburdened of nature's blind
demands— of no matter how and where, and to whom—
empty it into something!— was able to let float back into his
heart a slender recognition of a person with whom he had
shared an evening, from the first dance, all smiles and jokes
and carefulness to its ultimate shameful ending.'

She went weekly to the same dance hall with the twisting
glass chandelier in the centre, and whereas a few years
ago was always accompanied by her friend Doris— Doris
having got engaged and then well and truly pregnant, made
it necessary for her to go alone … All her friends got boy
friends one by one and although at first she wouldn't go alone
and went to the pictures instead, she found the dark wombs
of the cinema too unbearable and hated the end when she'd
walk home, made even lonelier by the romantic and exciting
lives of the screen heroes. One day she decided to go by
herself to the Mecca dance hall and since Mecca is the holy
and religious centre of the world, the salvation for an entire
race, it seemed natural that she would find solace there …on
occasion she would bump into her friends with their fellers
and join them at their table, but always felt slightly oppressed
by their little knowing glances which she'd exaggerate into

hideous thoughts of 'what's the slag doing by herself' ...and she would gradually recline to the outer perimeter of the dance floor ...in the shade so to speak and be dragged out to dance by one lonely man after another who first would eye her suspiciously and nervously. How a woman alone is a stigma ...and yet attractive ... dangerous, why alone? They think ... something in her casts her out from the norm ... the giggling girls ... the confident groups ... something that makes her slightly unwholesome, as if diseased ...yet offers up sweet, sickly goods if you want to take the risk ... still the element of danger ... makes her sought after by the kind of men whom the robust directness of youth would wilt ...who would not risk the light-hearted rebuff of young girls sure of their attractiveness who are waiting for strong, just as direct, young men ...but the lone figure in taffeta, now that is for me, man thinks, poses no threat ...only the remote element of a more nagging threat; no outward risk of humiliation ... possibly through the inward one, working on the vitals of the body or brain ...She moaned inside herself ... 'how unnatural that I am a leper just because my mother had a raging mouth' ...the two things were somehow now inseparable, as if her mother had really cursed a twisted fate on her that she could not untangle ... so rather and try and change this situation she would make her mother eat her satisfaction. 'I like it here,' she mused ... Through the years she had watched the faces grow up from tender, young, energetic and pretty things to smart (still young), mascaraed ladies, teasing and jiving with their beaux and it gave her not the slightest taste of jealousy or remorse ... she was glad that she felt no bitterness but was able to enjoy the gaiety, even if the young and pretty

things eyed her suspiciously as she, strange, caked make-up, wallflower smelling too violently of lavender water, waited.

One night early in the spring there was a warm snap in the air ... it was the first time she could go out without the heavy top-coat and thus be spared the awful queue after the dance when she would have to stand with all the chattering excited girls giggling about who was taking them home and exchanging notes ... If she hadn't found anyone to take her home, she as often as not would persist right to the end of the evening when most people had been paired off. She would nervously await the remnants of mankind, the lonely and the plain, or the just plain psychotic who, also unlucky, would desperately eye the last possibilities and the old tired wrecks to sort some salvage from the human female shapes that littered the outer ring. They, poor single women would feel even more vulnerable at this stage and creep nearer each other as if they too had friends, or ask each other for lights, pass nervous small smiles at each other, but still keep alert, since to pass out of the Mecca with a gentleman still hooked to your arm was still something worth waiting for ... not to go alone and leave alone ... show them— the young, the proud, the pretty— that I too can claim some happiness. So feeling spared of the queue and in the optimism that Spring brings, she was determined that night not to wait until the end and if nothing suitable came along, damn it— she'd go home. She went to the box-office clutching her money and set it down 'one please', but this time, and she did sense something as one man in an ill-fitting tuxedo leaned over the ear of the cashier, sense something like a cold blast? She did.

For the lady in the box office said … 'I'm so sorry dear but I'm afraid you're barred' … The queue of people behind her stopped their eager chattering, except for one joker, innocently unaware of the respect that one must pay in the face of tragedy, who sang 'Oh why are we waiting', to the tune of 'Oh Come All Ye Faithful' … 'So sorry,' the lady repeated … 'What have I done,' she thought, 'what have I done except act as a host to all those multitudes, to ease their agony …like a comfort station you might say, *something you need when you're desperate* …' She stood there as if the world had jolted to a halt and there could be no place you could possibly go since one's home was now a ruin of unmatchable stones …she couldn't speak …stood there as if it hadn't happened as if the cashier would witness the terrible effect which needed no words and would be humbled by the naked show of human agony and permit her to enter what now indeed seemed like a Mecca. She didn't, she just looked …and eventually said, 'Would you like to see the Manager?' but then as if annoyed by the inordinate amount of time this trivial incident was taking, the man in the box-office, who usually doubled as a bouncer, nipped nimbly out and took her to one side to let in the queue that had grown considerably. They all glanced at her half curious, half hostile … what's the slut done now? scrawled across their eyes … the man in the tuxedo spoke quietly, 'We don't want any trouble but you're barred ducky …alright …know what I mean …nothing personal like' …thought she, 'What did they suspect me of? What did they suspect could be my reasons over all these years for coming here … "Commerce" …is what's in their filthy minds?' … she said nothing … she had become in minutes flint from

velvet ... He continued but sensed a pain in her he hadn't
expected ...especially from a scrubber ... 'Give the place
a bad name, on the game you know ...get rid of it.' Higher
orders had thus embellished his mind with such commands
that he uncomfortably obeyed. 'You know,' he added
sympathetically, 'there's a club down the road called "The
Carousel", you'll be OK there.' He made the suggestion based
on the assumption that what he heard was true and therefore
his advice was charitable and not vicious. She knew the place
it was, and read only venom in his words and from that instant
began to hate the male part of the human race. She walked
away from the Mecca with it's twisting globe and ladies'
invitation waltzes with the familiar sound that same band
always had, from the familiar smell and initial excitement
when your first enter that huge cavern wherein may lie your
future ...she walked away from it ...for ever ....
She stayed home for a year until poor dad, perhaps willingly,
seeing his treasured forty year old daughter's plight, gave up
the ghost in one almighty shriek of joy.

She left home, determined to find that love-laced sanctuary
with a nice kitchen and sofa and saved for a record player. For
now, rents being high she lived in a bed-sitter and found that
loneliness just suddenly doesn't disappear ...when you have
lived with it for so long it emanates from your entire being
...when introduced even, you are afraid that the stranger will
sense it on you, as if some disagreeable odour lingers that
cannot be washed out. Sometimes, though rarely, she was
hauled away when her local closed for an after drink party,
more to make up the number than any cognisance of her being

…let alone her name …but still she was free …'aren't I,' she thought. Perhaps the caller on the telephone this evening is nice …I remember speaking to someone who was quite nice about a year ago at the office party …perhaps it's him …she sprayed some lavender water on her arms and not too carefully put her lipstick on …'hell, what can a girl do at ten p.m. when she's been sitting in drinking a few gins?'

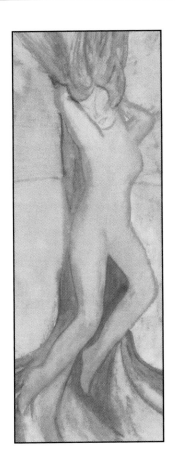

RUMORS (abridged)

by Harmony Korine

16.
Ray Harryhausen suffered from arthritis.

34.
Andy Kaufman used to put salt on his ice cream.

37.
Jerry Garcia tongue-kissed his older sister on her death bed.

40.
Jackson Pollack had a foot fetish.

56.
Kirk Douglas collects Pez dispensers.

61.
Isadora Duncan once scolded a homeless man
for having a swastika tattooed on his forearm.

43.
Emily Brontë used to ride her horse to a special place on the
side of a mountain. She would sit and eat her licorice and dream
of far-off places.

TOMMY
by
Rudyard Kipling

I went into a public-'ouse to get a pint o' beer,
The publican 'e up an sez, 'We serve no red-coats here.'
The girls be'ind the bar they laughed an' giggled fit to die,
I outs into the street again an' to myself sez I :
    O it's Tommy this, an' Tommy that, an' 'Tommy, go
        away';
    But it's 'Thank you, Mister Atkins,' when the band
        begins to play—
    The band begins to play, my boys, the band begins to
    play,
    O it's 'Thank you, Mister Atkins,' when the band
    begins to play.

I went into a theatre as sober as could be,
They gave a drunk civilian room, but 'adn't none for me;
They sent me to the gallery or round the music-'alls,
But when it comes to fightin', Lord! they'll shove me in
    the stalls!
    For it's Tommy this, an' Tommy that, an' 'Tommy,
      wait outside' ;
    But it's 'Special train for Atkins' when the trooper's
    on the tide—
    The troopship's on the tide, my boys, the troopship's
      on the tide—
    O it's 'Special train for Atkins' when the trooper's on
    the tide.

Yes, makin' mock o' uniforms that guard you while you
     sleep
Is cheaper than them uniforms, an' they're starvation
     cheap;
An hustlin' drunken soldiers when they're goin' large a
     bit
Is five times better business than paradin' in full kit.
     Then it's Tommy this, 'an Tommy that, an' 'Tommy,
        'ow's yer soul?'
    But it's 'Thin red line of 'eroes' when the drums begins
       to roll—
   The drums begin to roll, my boys, the drums begin to
      roll,
  O it's 'Thin red line of 'eroes' when the drums begin
     to roll.

We aren't no thin red 'eroes, nor we aren't no blackguards
     too,
But single men in barricks, most remarkable like you;
An' if sometimes our conduck isn't all your fancy paints,
Why, single men in barricks don't grow into plaster
     saints;
    While it's Tommy this, an 'Tommy that, an' 'Tommy,
       'fall be'ind,'
   But it's 'Please to walk in front, sir,' when there's
     trouble in the wind—
  There's trouble in the wind, my boys, there's trouble
    in the wind,
 O it's 'Please to walk in front, sir,' when there's
     trouble in the wind.

You talk o'better food for us, an' schools, an' fires, an'all:
We'll wait for extry rations if you treat us rational.
Don't mess about the cook-room slops, but prove it to our face.
The Widow's Uniform is not the soldier man's disgrace.
  For its Tommy this, an' tommy that, an' 'Chuck
      him out, the brute!'
  But it's saviour of 'is country' when the guns begin
      to shoot;
  An' it's Tommy this, an' Tommy that, an' anything
      you please;
  An' Tommy ain't a bloomin' fool—you bet that
      Tommy sees!

THE TRAVELLING COMPANION

Lord Alfred Douglas (1899)

Into the silence of the empty night
I went, and took my scorned heart with me,
And all the thousand eyes of heaven were bright;
But Sorrow came and led me back to thee.

I turned my weary eyes towards the sun,
Out of the leaden East like smoke came he.
I laughed and said, 'The night is past and done';
But Sorrow came and led me back to thee.

I turned my face towards the rising moon,
Out of the south she came most sweet to see,
She smiled upon my eyes that loathed the noon;
But Sorrow came and led me back to thee.

I bent my eyes upon the summer land,
And all the painted fields were ripe for me,
And every flower nodded to my hand;
But Sorrow came and led me back to thee.

O Love! O Sorrow! O desired Despair!
I turn my feet towards the boundless sea,
Into the dark I go and heed not where,
So that I come again at last to thee.

END.......

Poems for the retired nihilist

published by Fortune Teller Press,

2005

www.fortunetellerpress.com